The Common Dormouse

Elaine Hurrell

BLANDFORD PRESS

Poole   Dorset

G000115861

Contents

Illustration Credits

Cover Fritz Gehringer; A. J. Bond/Aquilla page 6; M. Clark 11; D. Corke 14, 23, 34, 43 (top); R. Hosking 2, 18, 19, 35; E. Hurrell 3; G. Kinns frontispiece; P. Livesley 7, 31; T. H. Maddock 43 (bottom); A. T. Moffet 22; O. Newman 15, 42; J. Preedy 10, 26, 27, 30, 38, 39.

Picture Editors Michael Clark   David Corke

Art Work Michael Clark

First published in Great Britain in 1980 by Blandford Press in association with The Mammal Society

Copyright © 1980 Blandford Press Ltd,
Link House, West Street,
Poole, Dorset, BH15 1LL

ISBN 0 7137 0985 5

British Library Cataloguing in Publication Data

Hurrell, Elaine
  The common dormouse.
  1. Dormice
  I. Title II. Mammal Society
  599'.3233   QL737. R656

Printed in Great Britain by Purnell & Sons Ltd, Paulton (Bristol) and London

Introduction

Dormice are small rodents with soft, orange-brown fur and long tails of a similar colour which are furred all over. They are such attractive animals that many people would like to be able to watch them but because they are almost entirely nocturnal this presents a challenge to observers.

The main chance of seeing one would be at twilight when many changes are taking place. For almost all birds it is the time to go to roost and to finish the day's activities but for many mammals it is the reverse: they are beginning their main spell of activity.

On a calm evening as the light fades and everything becomes quiet a stillness seems to settle over the countryside. Yet this is deceptive for it is just at this time that nocturnal mammals are on the move. Bats appear on the wing and in a thick habitat of hazel bushes and bramble cover a dormouse may emerge from its nest. By looking up at the leaf canopy against the evening sky it is sometimes possible to detect the tiny silhouette of a dormouse crossing the lighter spaces between the leaves. It may well be only a glimpse since dormice are capable of moving with surprising speed. They travel as smoothly as shadows up and down the stems and seem almost to flit as they cross from twig to twig.

Watching dormice in their natural surroundings—making direct observations in the wild—is not easy. It needs persistence and some luck as well as skill. It is easier to look for signs of their presence—making use of indirect evidence—such as remains of food and nests.

Frontispiece
Dormice are very adept at climbing on twigs and branches. Their feet are well adapted for such climbing and grasping and their tails are additional aids for balancing.

Description

In Britain this small mammal is known as the common dormouse but a more appropriate name could well be the hazel dormouse. Its scientific (Latin) name *Muscar-*

Dormice weave their nests using strippings of honeysuckle bark, grass, moss and leaves according to which materials are readily available in the habitat.

dinus avellanarius shows a connection with hazel. (The common hazel tree's scientific name is *Corylus avellana*.) Dormouse in German is *Haselmaus*—another connection with hazel—and in French it is *Muscardin*. The fact that the dormouse hibernates (goes into an inactive state in winter) is reflected in some of the local English names. In the counties of Hampshire and Cornwall it is

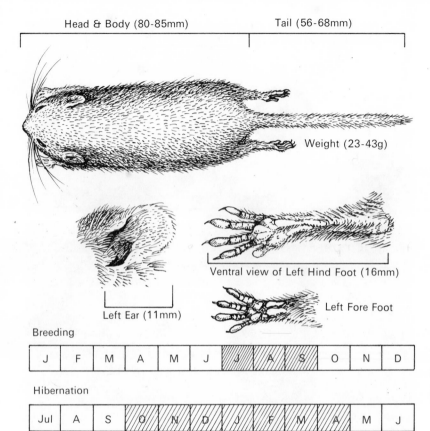

Head & Body (80-85mm) Tail (56-68mm)

Weight (23-43g)

Ventral view of Left Hind Foot (16mm)

Left Ear (11mm)

Left Fore Foot

Breeding

J	F	M	A	M	J	J	A	S	O	N	D

Hibernation

Jul	A	S	O	N	D	J	F	M	A	M	J

Fig.1 *Measurements and breeding season for the British Common Dormouse population.*

known as 'dory-mouse' and 'dozing mouse' respectively; in many counties it is known as the 'sleeper', the 'seven sleeper' or 'sleep-mouse'. Its attractive appearance has a fairy-tale charm and other delightful local. names include 'chestle-crumb' and 'derry-mouse'.

Dormice belong to the mammalian order Rodentia and to the family Gliridae. (Rats and mice belong to the family Muridae.) Dormice have four upper and lower cheek-teeth whereas rats and mice only have three.

The tooth patterns of crosswise ridges on the molar

teeth are distinctive to the dormouse and therefore important for identification.

The head and body measured together are 80-85 mm and the tail is 56-68 mm. The weight varies from 23 to 43 g according to the time of year. A dormouse is heaviest just before it starts hibernating.

It is readily distinguished from other mice by its rounded, compact shape and, more especially, by its orange-brown coat and thickly furred tail. The general impression is of a light coloured animal, although, in fact, the orange-brown fur on its upper parts has a fine sprinkling of darker hairs but these are thinly scattered. The tip of the tail may also be darker. The underparts are much paler, sometimes pure white. Young dormice are much greyer, the rich colouring of the adult coming only during the first winter, while the animal is hibernating. Albino dormice—white all over—are rare but dormice with white tips to the tail are recorded a little more often.

The most striking features of the head are the fine, black whiskers—these may be 25-30 mm long—and the large, prominent black eyes. When moving about in the dark, the very long whiskers are used as sense organs; they quiver repeatedly when the animal is still. The ears are not large but rounded, showing clearly above the fur.

Dormice spend a lot of time climbing about amongst branches and twigs. They are very well adapted to arboreal (tree) life. Their front limbs are short. Both front and back feet are prehensile (capable of grasping) and, as the front feet can be turned out sideways—almost at right angles to the body—twigs and branches can be clasped firmly and easily. The furry tail is not prehensile.

The dormouse has four fully developed digits (fingers or toes) on each foot and there is a gap

A wren builds a spherical nest but it can be distinguished from that of a dormouse by examining the entrance hole. The wren uses small twigs and grass stalks to weave a 'doorstep' across the base of the hole.

An adult dormouse. The furry tail is frequently held in a curved position like the one in this picture.

separating the fourth and fifth digit on the hind feet. The digits are long and slender and covered with short downy fur on the upper surfaces; they end in strong short claws. On the under surfaces there are well-developed pads which help the animal to keep a firm grip as it climbs.

7

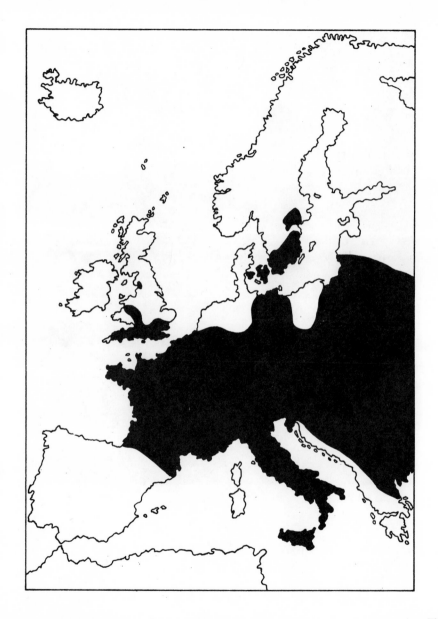

Fig. 2 *European distribution of the Common Dormouse.*

Distribution

The hazel dormouse, a European mammal, is found from the woods of Sweden in the north to the slopes of the Alps in the south. It is not found in Spain or Denmark but is found eastwards to the Volga and into Asia Minor. It is regarded as a comparative newcomer to the British fauna, having spread westwards from south central Europe during the Pleistocene Age, less than a million years ago. There are many fossil remains of dormice on the European continent but so far none appear to have been discovered in Britain.

At present it is found in England and Wales but not in Scotland or Ireland. In Wales it occurs in the border counties between Wales and England but only in local pockets elsewhere. In England it is found more often in southern counties than in the north. It is scarce in the Midlands and, although present in Sussex, Surrey, Kent and Essex and in a few places in Suffolk, eastern counties like Norfolk and Lincolnshire are not favoured. The northern limit of dormouse distribution in Britain at the beginning of this century was stated to be the county boundary between Durham and Northumberland. Today, it seems unlikely to be found so far north. When the current distribution survey organised by the Mammal Society has been completed we should have a much clearer idea of the present northern limit of its range and its current status.

Dormice seem to occur in small concentrations or pockets. We do not know why, but if two apparently similar and equally suitable areas are searched, it is quite possible that dormice will be found in one area and yet be totally absent from the other.

There is no doubt that today the dormouse is not as common as it once was. It is likely that numbers have been going down for some time. Even during the second half of the last century it was thought to have

The Grey Dormouse (Glis glis) was introduced into Britain and, unlike the Common Dormouse, is regarded by the Forestry Commission as a potential pest.

declined in South Devon. During the present century a number of changes in farming and forestry methods have been harmful to dormice. Areas of scrub or marginal land have been cleared and hedges have either been removed or repeatedly slashed with mechanical trimmers. These practices have disturbed and destroyed places where dormice might have nested. Young hazel wood used to be much in demand for making stakes, hurdles and even pea sticks. Now it is not wanted for everyday use. Coppicing has virtually died out as a regular forestry operation and hazel is no longer planted for taking quick crops. Man changes his habits and the dormouse loses some of its best places to live.

10

Habitat

Dormice prefer to live in a shrub layer which has plenty of undergrowth. Examples of this kind of site are woodland edges, young plantations, rough commons, thick hedges and overgrown gardens. Thick, tangled undergrowth may include plants like brambles, willow-herb and honeysuckle. Taller shrubs may include hazel

11

or guelder rose as well as young trees. Dormice do not favour tall, mature woodland itself but prefer the edges or clearings. For this reason the dormouse can be thought of as a 'woodland edge' animal. In a wood full of tall trees, the leaves shut out the sunlight and the close canopy discourages undergrowth. Woodland goes through various stages of growth and as dormice prefer the transitional stage—before the trees become fully mature—they must be able to move on and colonise new areas from time to time.

There are a few records of dormice being found with no hazel nearby, but of all the plants mentioned hazel has the closest association with the dormouse. The habitat must provide it with food and appropriate shelter. Hazel nuts, sweet-chestnuts, wild cherries, acorns, blackberries and raspberries all provide a rich diet in late summer and autumn before hibernation.

The denseness of the shrub layer provides protection against its enemies as well as suitable nest sites. The taller shrubs provide not only food but also suitable levels for travelling through their territory. Obviously, the mice thrive best in relatively undisturbed areas. This is particularly important in a species where the young mice have to remain in the breeding nest for a month. In some areas, deserted or undisturbed gardens have provided records for the current survey which is being carried out in Britain. At least two records come from bramble thickets in the grounds of ruined castles.

Field Signs
The most reliable signs of the presence of dormice include nests, the stripping of bark from honeysuckle stems and a characteristic way of opening hazel nuts. Droppings, too, may occasionally be helpful.

Dormice usually have three kinds of nests which are

used for different purposes: breeding nests, shelter nests and hibernation nests. The summer breeding nest is domed and can be up to 15 cm in diameter. It is rather bulky and the largest nest made by a dormouse. Often the main material used is strippings from honeysuckle stems or dry grass, and incorporated in this are leaves such as bramble or hazel. The finished structure appears loosely woven, rather untidy in general appearance and often without any definite entrance. By contrast, a typical wren's nest has an entrance hole which is distinct, made so by the fact that the wren constructs at the base of the hole a kind of 'doorstep' of firmly woven grass and fine twigs. The dormouse uses very thinly shredded material near the centre and some of this material is sometimes pulled out with the animal as it leaves the nest. A breeding female mouse may have more than one nest and if she is severely disturbed will move the young to one of the other nests. Once the young are old enough to scatter from the breeding nest, they construct their own shelter nests; these may be fairly close together but are usually occupied singly and are smaller in size.

Frequently nests are built at about a metre from the ground where bramble stems cross each other horizontally. The nest is constructed on the stems and if a disused nest is examined, the groove where it rested on the stems can quite easily be seen. In other vegetation the height of the nest sites is very variable.

Hibernation nests may be sited inside a hollow tree, in a hole under the ground or under a thick carpet of leaves on the ground itself. Dormice have been found in deep hibernation in bird boxes and in old birds' nests. The height at which these hibernation nests are found varies widely, from ground level to as much as 12 metres above ground. The examination of honeysuckle for the delicate stripping of quite tiny stems can suggest

a nearby nest. Other animals, such as the grey squirrel, may strip the bark but their work tends to be coarser and more extensive.

The way a dormouse opens a hazel nut has proved to be the most valuable of all field signs since it differs from the methods used by other small mammals. Woodmice and bank voles make a corrugated edge

around the inside of the hole. The dormouse produces a neat round hole on one side of the nut but the special characteristic is that the edge of the hole is not corrugated but smoothly chiselled in a circular fashion. This smooth, inside edge has been made by the lower incisors working away at the shell as the nut was rotated. Outside this chiselled edge small scratch marks can be

15

seen; these were made by the upper incisors as they gripped the shell. When checking these nuts in the field it is helpful to use a magnifying lens or to turn one's binoculars around and look at the nuts through the 'wrong' end.

The methods used by different small mammals have been checked by feeding hazel nuts to captive bank voles, wood mice and dormice and comparing opened nuts.

Besides nutshells and nests, further field signs include recognising the animal's droppings. These may be found on the top of a nest which has been used by the animal as a platform. In their general shape the droppings are less uniform than those of other mice. They have a rougher surface and often look twisted or plaited. In particular they are very variable in size, some being very small, even less than 1 mm across, and others much larger. An exceptionally large one was 15 mm in length and 3 mm in width. Most often their colour is black but they can also be paler with a greenish or yellow tinge, this no doubt depending on diet.

Behaviour

A small, nocturnal mammal which lives in dense undergrowth and bushes is not easy to study in the wild, nor is it easy to provide it with similar natural conditions in captivity. Yet, using both approaches, more and more information is being collected. How they move, how far they move, what their annual rhythm of activity and inactivity is like, the way they communicate and the senses they have—all these are interesting aspects of behaviour to investigate.

After watching dormice for many hours in captivity it is a complete revelation to see them in the wild. This is particularly so when watching the way they move. In the wild their skill at running along branches and threading their way through leafy canopies is quite breath-taking. Twilight is usually the only time when there is enough light to discover them in the leaf canopy when they appear moving overhead as a tiny round shape with a straight tail. Often they may be impossible to see against the leaves and seem to vanish, but then they are picked up again as a silhouette against the sky, crossing the gaps between leaves. At times they appear and disappear so quickly before one's eyes it is as if one is watching a series of conjuring tricks. Sometimes they repeatedly glide down and up vertical stems like the action of a yo-yo.

Watching them at twilight it is clear that they have routes which they know well and which they race over again and again. No doubt they are just as capable of following these familiar routes even when it is really dark. Yet often, for all the smoothness of their movement along stems or branches, there is also something jerky and erratic about their progress. They may jump 30 cm or so from twig to twig and then, quite suddenly, stop and freeze for seconds or even minutes. This ability to freeze appears to be a means of avoiding detection by natural enemies.

Using a torch with a red cellophane filter, because nocturnal animals react less to red light, it is still rarely possible to spot a dormouse after dark even when one is known to be close by or can be heard opening a nut overhead. The layers of leaves hide them very effectively. The first indication that a nut is being eaten by a dormouse will be the pattering sound of the calyx (the small 'cup' holding the nut) being stripped off and dropping to the ground. It sounds like a gentle sprinkling of rain. Following this there is a distinctive chiselling sound which continues intermittently. This can be heard up to a distance of about 20 metres and is like the

Getting inside a hazelnut shell is hard work! The sound of the chiselling can be heard up to a distance of about 20 metres.

The dormouse uses its front feet to rotate the hazelnut as its lower incisors chisel through the shell.

This sleeping dormouse is evidently a captive animal since wild dormice are not likely to store food where they hibernate.

sound of a nail file being used vigorously or a finger nail being rubbed repeatedly against the ribbed edge of a coin. In fact, it is made by the action of the lower incisors of the dormouse against the shell of the hazel nut. The nut is held in its paws while it sits in an almost upright position, high up in the hazel. It seems usual for dormice to bite off the nuts before selecting a place where they will sit to open them. At twilight it has been possible to note carefully the kind of position they select. They can be seen pitched on the side of slanting hazel stems just below the canopy of leaves and at other times sitting on a horizontal twig in the canopy with the tail hanging down like a tiny bell rope. The nut is rotated rapidly by the front paws as the lower incisors chisel away. Periodically, the chiselling ceases as small amounts of kernel are extracted by its teeth and eaten. It can take up to 15 minutes for the complete kernel to be eaten and then the discarded nutshell can be heard falling down through the leaves and sharply hitting the ground.

The distribution of opened nutshells by small mammals also varies. Dormice open nuts in the canopy and drop the empty shells from this position. The shells can be found scattered, often hole side upward, underneath the bush. Both bank voles and wood mice eat hazel nuts on the ground and very often these will be found in hordes where they have been collected together. I have watched a wood mouse bringing a cluster of hazel nuts, which it carried in its mouth, down to the ground. It made an amusing picture, the nut cluster looking like very thick whiskers! Evidently it was not prepared to sit in the bush and eat it like a dormouse.

More information is needed about the dormouse's pattern of activity through the night. There are some indications which point to a first peak of activity from twilight for an hour or two and another considerably

An attractively coloured small mammal, the dormouse grooms its fur meticulously and completes the job by combing minutely through its long, furred tail.

later around 2 to 4 in the morning.

There is evidence that the furthest distance of a dormouse's eating place from its nest is about 40 metres but it is thought that usually the animals move no more than about 10 metres for their food.

Grooming is an important activity and dormice in captivity will spend a considerable time going through

The top nut shows the smooth edge after a dormouse has chiselled a hole in a hazelnut. It presents a definite contrast to the corrugated effect left by a Wood Mouse as shown in the nut at the bottom of the picture.

*Smaller than a Grey Squirrel, the
Grey Dormouse has a thickly
furred tail and prominent eyes.
The Romans fattened them for
the table in jars called Gliraria.*

their fur very minutely, no doubt using both tongue and teeth. They rub behind their heads and ears with their small front paws and then work over their eyes and noses. Finally they reach round to comb vigorously through the fur on their backs and then bring up in front of them their long, furry tails and groom these meticulously.

Hibernation

The dormouse is a rodent which hibernates. This has come about presumably to enable it to live in a climate which is unfavourable during the winter months. In preparation for hibernation the dormouse builds itself a winter nest which may be at ground level under the leaf litter or in a tree stump. Sometimes a bird nesting box or a specially designed small mammal box will provide a suitable site for hibernation. As the autumn proceeds the dormouse becomes very fat, eating plenty of autumn fruits and hazel nuts. The latter are extremely important as they contain a large amount of protein and fat. Although much has been written about the storage of food in preparation for the winter there is little evidence of dormice doing this.

Hibernation appears to be brought on by the accumulation of fat, for neither low temperatures nor the scarcity of food appear to be its primary cause. The dormouse retires to its winter nest where it rolls itself into a very neat ball. Its hind feet are clenched and curled forward level with its nose, while its front feet are also clenched but held under its chin. Its eyes are tightly shut and the ears are folded back against the head while the tail is wrapped around the body, covering its face and a part of its back. The breathing is scarcely detectable except from time to time when there is a thin, whistling, wheezing sound as the air is breathed out.

The animal has become a small, compact, tightly-rolled-up ball utterly oblivious to all that is happening.

As the dormouse sinks into this state of torpidity (inactivity) its breathing and heart rate fall and the temperature decreases so much that the animal feels cold to the touch. Hibernation usually lasts from October to April but sleep may be interrupted and dormice may wake and leave the nest for feeding. Sometimes what is called 'partial arousal' also occurs. When this happens the nest temperature increases but the animal does not leave the nest.

By the time that the dormouse emerges from hiber-

More young dormice. They first leave the nest at about a month old.

nation its body weight will have fallen by almost half. The fat stored in the body will have been used up in producing the minimal amount of energy needed for breathing and maintaining the body temperature above freezing point. Those dormice which hibernated as juveniles will emerge with adult pelage (fur) of orange-brown and will be ready to breed during the season following hibernation.

No wonder the dormouse, with its ability to hibernate for long periods, has become a symbol of drowsiness and comfortableness, and references in literature to its sleepiness are numerous. Thus, we read that the guests who came to the tea party in *Alice's Adventures in Wonderland* by Lewis Carroll found the dormouse a delightful if somewhat drowsy companion. At one point the conversation goes like this:

> 'You might just as well say,' added the Dormouse, who seemed to be talking in his sleep, 'that "I breathe when I sleep" is the same thing as "I sleep when I breathe"!'
> 'It *is* the same thing with you,' said the Hatter . . .

All the way through that famous party the Dormouse had to be nudged and pinched to keep him awake!

Communication

Although dormice can normally be thought of as quiet mammals they do make a variety of sounds. Captive animals provide opportunities to hear some of these. One breeding female kept in a colony seemed disturbed by the presence of other dormice near her nest and produced a plaintive, mewing call which resembled the distant food call of a young sparrowhawk. The sound went on for several minutes and could easily be heard several metres away. On another occasion two dormice before mating made short, squeaking sounds. Situations where there is chasing or conflict may also produce high-pitched squeaks. Certainly in the wild when dormice are chasing each other little bat-like twitters are sometimes audible.

Another sound which has been heard is a fluttering or whirring sound. So far this has been difficult to interpret but it has been noticed with captive dormice on more than one occasion prior to mating, as well as once in the wild. There is a characteristic wheezing sound made by a hibernating dormouse which is triggered off when the animal is moved and perhaps begins to awaken a little. There is an account of a keeper in Cornwall who used to locate dormice for children to keep as pets by listening for this sound near a sunny bank in early spring.

It is interesting to speculate about ultrasonic sounds (sounds inaudible to us) being made by dormice. On occasions it has seemed to me as if this was taking place as a means of communication between wild dormice.

Feeding

The diet of a dormouse during the spring when it emerges from hibernation is difficult to determine. There are few fruits and seeds to be found and few leaves, but perhaps the fresh young buds or shoots of various plants like honeysuckle may be used, and certainly honeysuckle flowers are eaten later in the year. It has been recorded that seeding heads of grasses are eaten and also the veins of leaves. My observations confirm that honeysuckle leaves are nibbled by dormice, especially the stalks of the leaves.

Towards autumn there can be no difficulty in finding food; blackberries, rowan berries, hazel nuts, acorns and beech mast are all eaten. Grapes, apples, cherries, raspberries, sunflower seeds and biscuits are eaten readily by captive dormice.

It is doubtful whether they are completely vegetarian, however, as they have been reported to eat insects such as aphids, nut weevils and various kinds of caterpillars.

Close-up of a dormouse's head showing its large, black eyes and long whiskers – both typical of an animal that is active at night.

Breeding

Young dormice are generally born between May and October. There are many instances of litters being observed into October and this suggests that the peak of the breeding season may occur late in the year. There has been much debate about whether the female has one or two litters each summer, but in captivity females have definitely been known to have two. Each litter consists of three, four or five young.

Gestation—the period between mating and birth—is 22-24 days, and when the young are born they weigh only 3 to 4 g. A newborn dormouse is both blind and naked and is said to be so underdeveloped in appearance that it gives the impression of a premature birth. After a week it has some colouring as pigmentation appears in the skin and the fur begins to grow. By 13 days the young dormouse is fully furred but still blind and it is not until it is 18 days old that it really can see. At 24 days old the young animal is well formed but a greyer colour than the adult, and by 30 days it is able to leave the nest. It is not until it is 40 days old that it is considered independent and then it will go away from the nest and not return, making its own nest in the vicinity. The young during their first summer still show a different coat from the adult; they will not develop the beautiful sandy colour of an adult until after the first winter's hibernation. By then it will be indistinguishable from the adult and sexually mature. It is said that the mice born late in the season are the ones which have late litters during the next season.

Life Span

The natural life span of a dormouse in the wild is unknown. One of our captive females lived for 4 years and another for 6 years, the latter equalling the age of a dormouse kept by Miss Frances Pitt, which is, of course, exceptional.

There are records of marked animals reaching 4 years of age in the wild. However, their normal life span is thought to be about 3 years, by which time the ridges on their molar teeth are well worn.

Predators and Mortality

There are very few records of dormouse remains in owl pellets and it seems likely that they are usually extremely difficult animals for owls to catch in the shrub layer of a wood. Information from a study area in Poland includes the fact that no remains of dormice were found in bird of prey nests nor in 50,000 owl pellets.

They are sometimes brought in by cats so there must be times when they come down on or near the ground for this to happen. Mr A. F. Tebbut describes a view he once had of a fox near his home in Sussex which was 'mousing' in long grass in an area where dormouse nests had been found. As he watched, the fox grabbed a small, light-coloured animal which he strongly suspected was a dormouse.

When they are hibernating, even though the scent given off would be minimal, they must be very vulnerable to predators. Weasels, stoats or foxes may come across them when foraging for food. A tightly-woven nest with its occupant alive but sound asleep inside was once found under a raven roost in a wood in south-west England. There are other records of crows and magpies discovering nests with hibernating dormice inside.

As well as the dangers from predation the state of hibernation must impose strains on the physical well-being of the dormouse itself. Unless it is thoroughly fit and in very good condition it may well not survive to see the spring. The Swiss naturalist Fritz Gehringer, in a spoken commentary to his superb film on the hazel dormouse, called *An 85 Day Year*, says, 'Hibernation is also a test of the condition of the rodent's organs, for a sick animal, or one that is too old, has little chance of seeing the spring again.'

Like bats, if the weather is mild and they wake too often, they use up their reserves of energy too quickly and are more likely to die. Certainly, captive dormice

A hibernating dormouse curls itself into a ball with its paws tucked in under its nose and with its furry tail wrapped over its head.

kept in conditions which are open to the weather suffer more losses in mild winters than in severe ones.

So it can be appreciated that the dormouse is especially vulnerable during the hibernation period and one study has suggested a population loss of as much as 80% during the winter.

The state of hibernation lasts off and on throughout the winter. The temperature drops, the heart-rate is reduced, it does not eat and it can survive like this for many weeks at a time.

Some of the dormouse's local names such as sevensleeper, dozing mouse and sleepmouse reflect its ability to be completely unaware of its surroundings for a large proportion of the year.

Relations with Man

The dormouse is such an attractively coloured and amenable small animal that at one time it was frequently kept as a pet. But, as a dormouse can be sluggish in temperament and only active at night, it must have been rather overrated. However, schoolboys in Victorian times were said to produce one from a pocket just as children today might exhibit a pet gerbil or hamster.

It is the ease with which the animal could be found in those days that interests us today. For instance it is told that in the Chilterns at the turn of the century a gamekeeper, if requested, could without difficulty bring in a dormouse, and then in a few weeks' time, when the novelty has worn off, release it. He would soon find another if it was wanted. This could not be done so readily today.

Frances Pitt, also writing at the turn of the century and referring to Shropshire, says that dormice were often picked up in the autumn but that since then the species has steadily decreased, until in 1940 she considered it was a rarity.

There seems little doubt that a real decline in numbers has taken place over the last seventy years and that the animal is much scarcer now than it was at the end of the last century. Indeed, the dormouse was nearly included in the schedule of the Protection of Wild Creatures legislation of 1975.

There are many of man's activities which are having a considerable effect on the lives of dormice. The mechanisation of agriculture is an important factor. We have seen that the severe cutting of hedges and in many cases their complete removal, as well as the clearance of scrub, is reducing habitats at an alarming rate. Marginal land reclamation, as well as the fact that hazel coppicing is no longer done on any large scale, are further factors which must be to the disadvantage of the dormouse,

37

Dormouse habitats often have plants which are prickly in them. It is remarkable how these mice manage to thread their way along stems bristling with thorns and prickles!

continuing to weaken its ability to survive.

The presence of grey squirrels in England and Wales, released there by man, is producing yet another pressure by introducing severe competition for fattening foods such as hazel nuts.

A dormouse, undeterred by thorns, climbing on wild rose stems.

Conservation

It is extremely important to conserve wherever possible the kinds of habitats in which dormice can flourish. A woodland edge with dense cover, even if small, is extremely valuable. Hedges which have a variety of shrubs, large deserted gardens or areas where bramble thickets are allowed to grow are all tremendously important to the species. Indeed, if one plant, apart from hazel, is important to dormice it is the bramble. Patches of bramble provide some of the most often used and secure habitats for dormice. Landowners who are able to conserve wild areas where dog-roses, brambles, willow-herb and gorse bushes can thrive are making a useful contribution, because they are safeguarding sites which could well attract dormice.

But since the dormouse requires a 'transitional' habitat the management of such areas is complex. For instance, growth must not become too mature, and measures like rotational coppicing, although seeming to disturb the species, will in the long run be of benefit. However, when carrying out a plan which includes cutting growth back at regular intervals, it is important to have adjacent suitable habitats for the dormice while the coppiced parts are recovering.

Another provision is to place small boxes, like tit boxes, on trees at varying heights with the entrance hole turned towards the trunk. These can be readily used by small mammals, which sometimes include dormice.

Conservation in the ways indicated above can be extremely valuable in helping to maintain places in which this very attractive small mammal can live its life and continue to be such a lively and specialised but particularly charming member of our European fauna.

Acknowledgements

I would like to thank Mrs G. M. McIntosh, Mr H. G. Hurrell and Dr L. H. Hurrell (my father and brother) and Dr B. E. Heine for their invaluable assistance in the preparation of this material; Mrs J. Johnson for typing the manuscript; Mr D. Stapleford for a number of personal communications and Dr H. N. Southern for lending me relevant proof sheets from the revised edition of *The Handbook of British Mammals* prior to its publication.

*Another view of this tiny,
acrobatic mammal.*